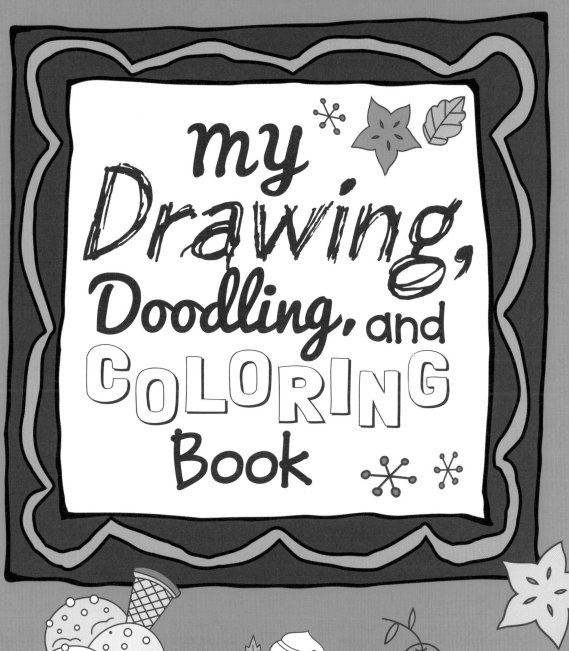

my Drawing, Doodling, and COLORING Book

ARCTURUS

ARCTURUS

This edition published in 2017 by Arcturus Publishing Limited
26/27 Bickels Yard, 151–153 Bermondsey Street,
London SE1 3HA

Designed by Amy McSimpson.
Text and picture research by Frances Evans.
The pictures in this book are by the following artists:
Laura Avino: 4-5, 12, 15, 32, 56, 62-63, 64, 82, 94-95, 98-99, 113, 118, 125, 144, 147,
152-153, 156-157, 169, 178, 184, 193, 196-197, 214, 224-225, 256.
Louise Forshaw: 18, 24, 43, 65, 68-69, 83, 86-87, 112, 124, 126, 128-129, 142, 159, 175,
179, 198-199, 215, 226-227.
Felicity French: 3, 19, 25, 36-37, 42, 44, 74, 76, 93, 106-107, 119, 135, 153, 162, 166-
167, 185, 189, 200-201, 204, 232, 234-235, 254-255.
Katie Saunders: 13, 28-29, 57, 75, 92, 136-137, 146, 168, 188, 192, 205, 218-219, 233.
All other pictures are taken from Shutterstock.

ISBN 978-1-78404-572-2
CH004563US
Supplier: 29, Date 0317, Print run 5932

Printed in China

The king and queen are holding a tournament!

Count the baby dragons and color them in.

Draw the tallest, tastiest ice cream sundae you can imagine!

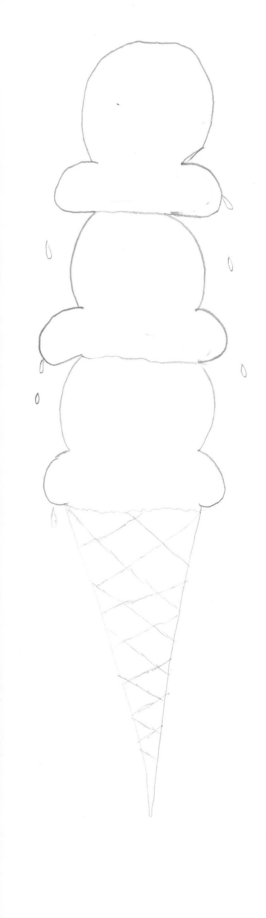

Color in these fancy cups and saucers.

Color in the funky pattern.

Doodle some more alien basketball players!

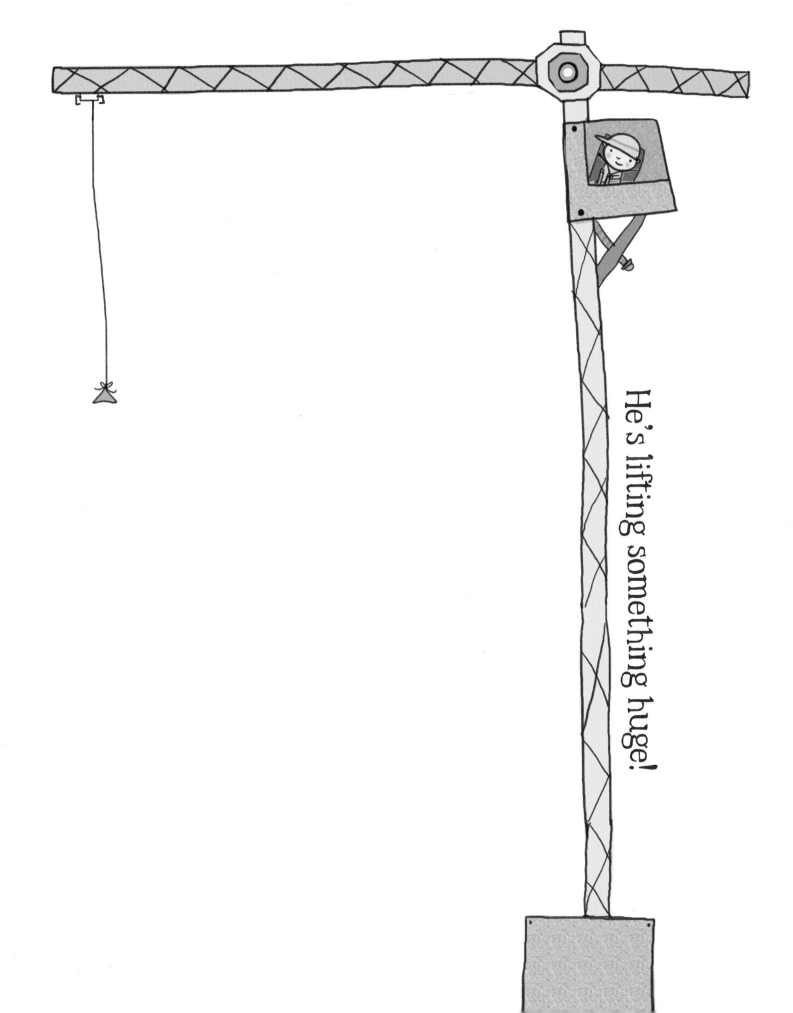

He's lifting something huge!

Draw the genie who lives in this lamp!

Color in these princesses, and doodle some accessories to match their gowns.

Color in this pretty egg, then design some of your own.

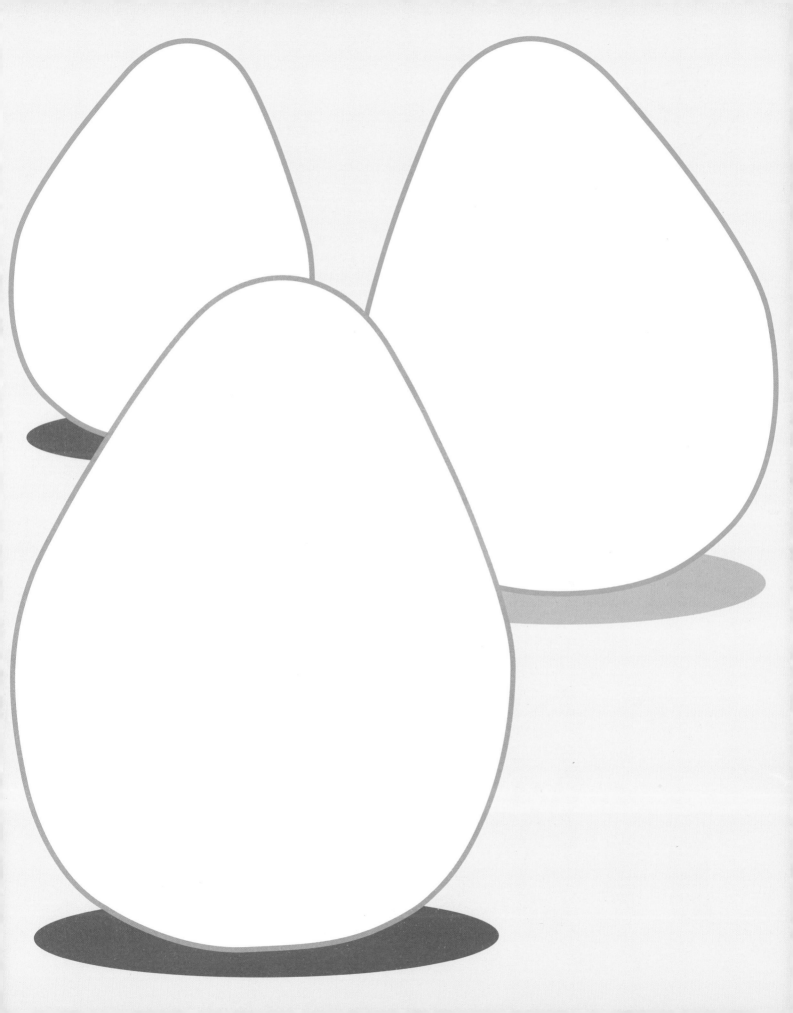

Draw your dream pet!

Fill this page with
a meadow for these
flower fairies.

Try using a different color for each line.

Doodle some more robots.

Color in the cats.

Draw a friend for this beautiful rhino.

Color the houses.

Color in the construction site!

Shade each wave a different color.

Doodle some more aliens stuck in traffic.

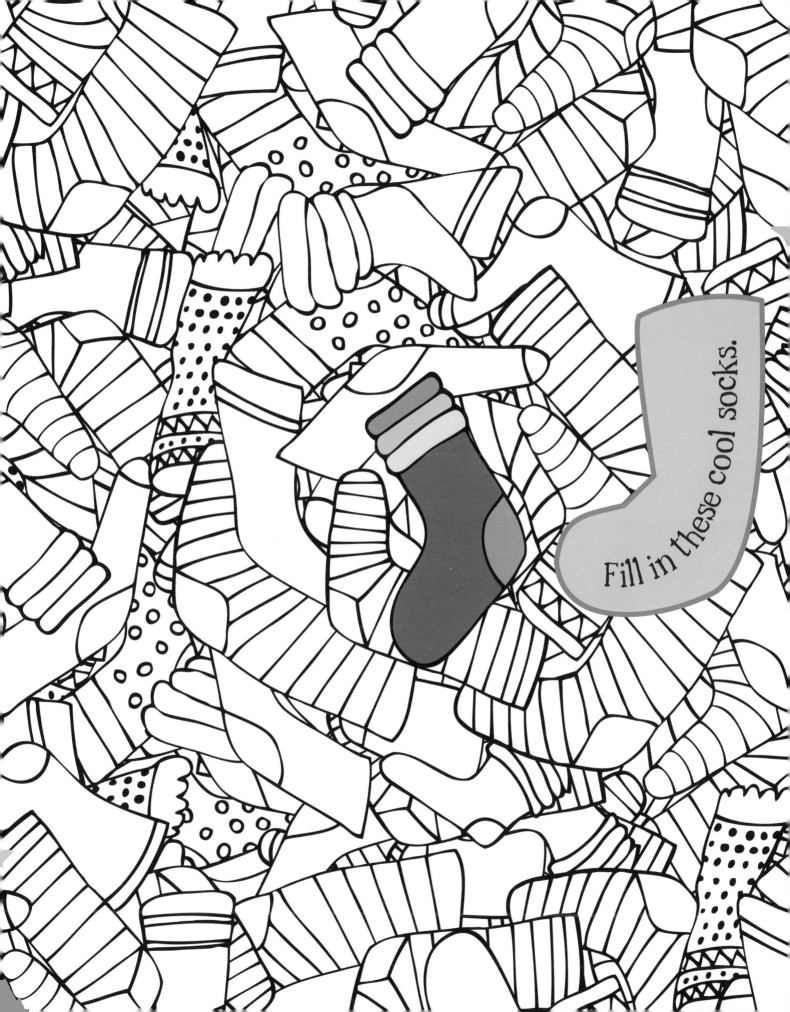

Fill in these cool socks.

Give these snails some super cool shells.

Fill this page with colorful kites!

Draw the scariest or cuddliest monster you can imagine.

How many saxophones can you see?

Color them in!

Draw a jungle for this monkey to swing in.

These eggs
are hatching!
Draw their
proud parents.

Who has been invited to the fairy tea party?

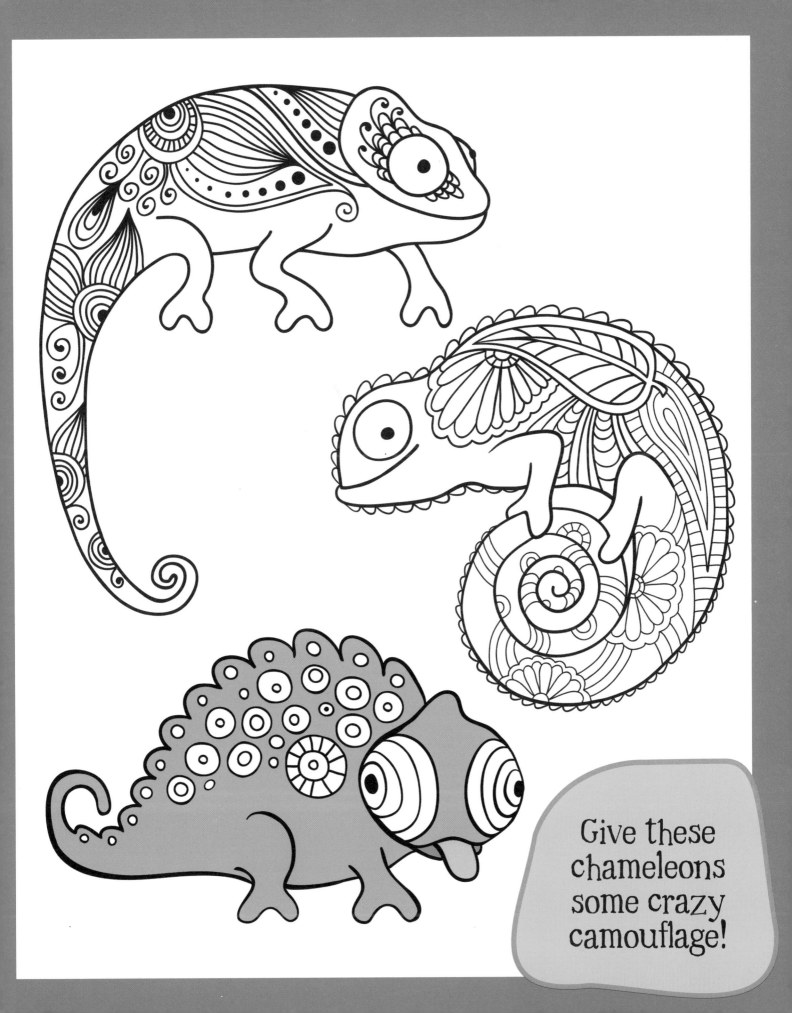

Give these chameleons some crazy camouflage!

Color in these hot air balloons...

...then draw what you think they're flying over.

Draw some snazzy shades.

Doodle some designs on these sneakers.

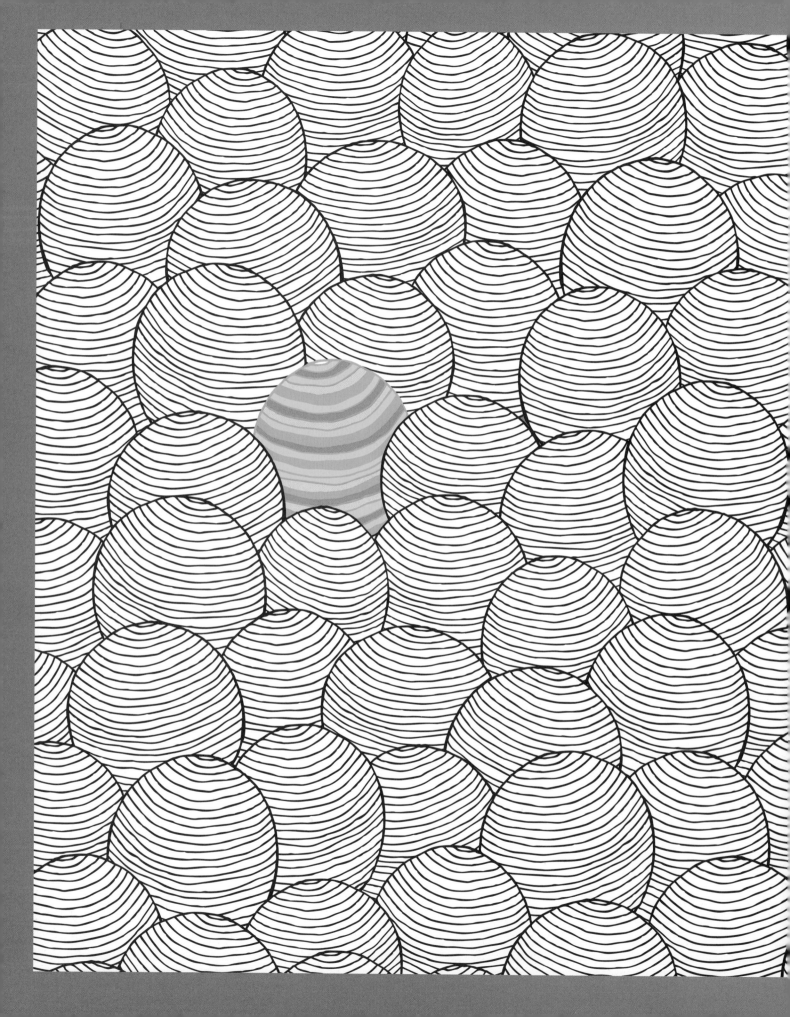

Choose some bright colors for these balls of yarn.

Color all the one-eyed monsters purple and green, then color in the rest.

Draw the other buildings on this Wild West street.

Draw some more astronaut mice, and a mouse-sized spaceship.

Color the cherries and lemons first, then color the rest.

Color in this leafy pattern.

EARTH

Color in this otherworldly scene!

Fill this page with turtles of all shapes and sizes!

Give these sheep some colorful coats.

Draw the prehistoric world that this Pterodactyl is flying over.

Fill in this pretty pattern.

Design some
Russian dolls.
Remember,
they come in
different sizes!

Fill this page with
African birds!

Color in this digger, then draw your favorite truck.

Draw some fairies having a rest on these toadstools.

Color these cassettes.

Draw a field full of teepees!

Finish off this totem pole, then design one of your own.

Use as many colors as you can to fill in these flowers.

Draw some
more
alien pets!

Doodle this hamster a huge store of food.

Color the tropical fish.

Color in these amazing dinos!

Color in the leaves.

That was a hard day's work! Draw a tasty dinner for these builders.

Color in these fairies and pixies!

What do you think this alien astronomer can see?

Who has stolen this knight's heart?

Give these lizards some spectacular scales!

Bullseye!
Finish the
medieval
scene...

Color in these supernovas.

Design some cool skateboards of your own.

Fill this page with beautiful flags!

Color these tribal masks.

Color in this Venetian mask, then design one of your own!

Color the trees for the sloths to swing in.

Color in the puppies and draw some more!

Color in the aliens.
Then draw alien versions
of your family!

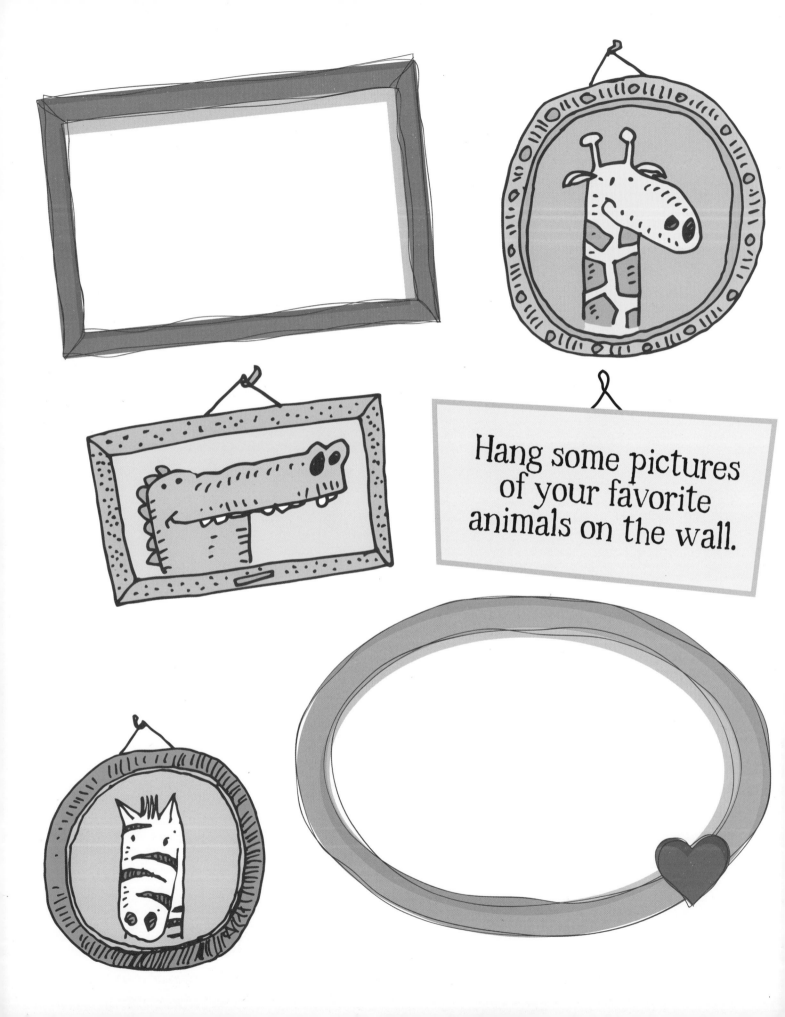

Hang some pictures of your favorite animals on the wall.

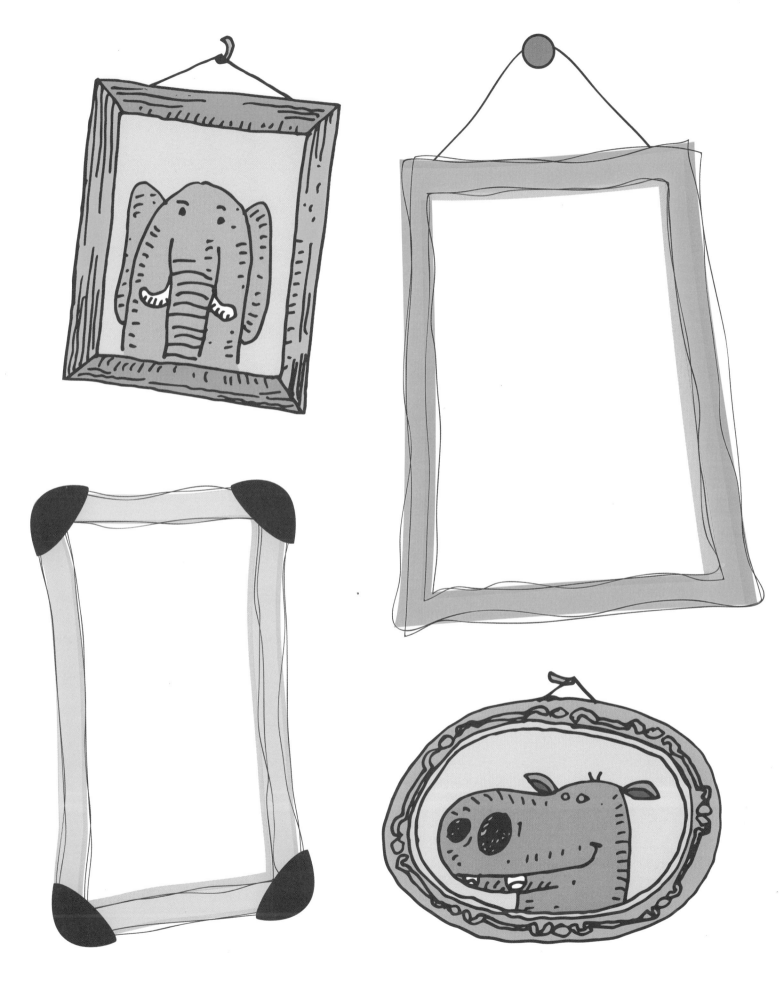

Howdy partner! Color in these cowboy boots.

Draw what the trolls' cave looks like.

What is this jester juggling?

Draw some other
woodland creatures
who are getting
makeovers.

Color in these beautiful corals!

Fill this page with pretty parasols.

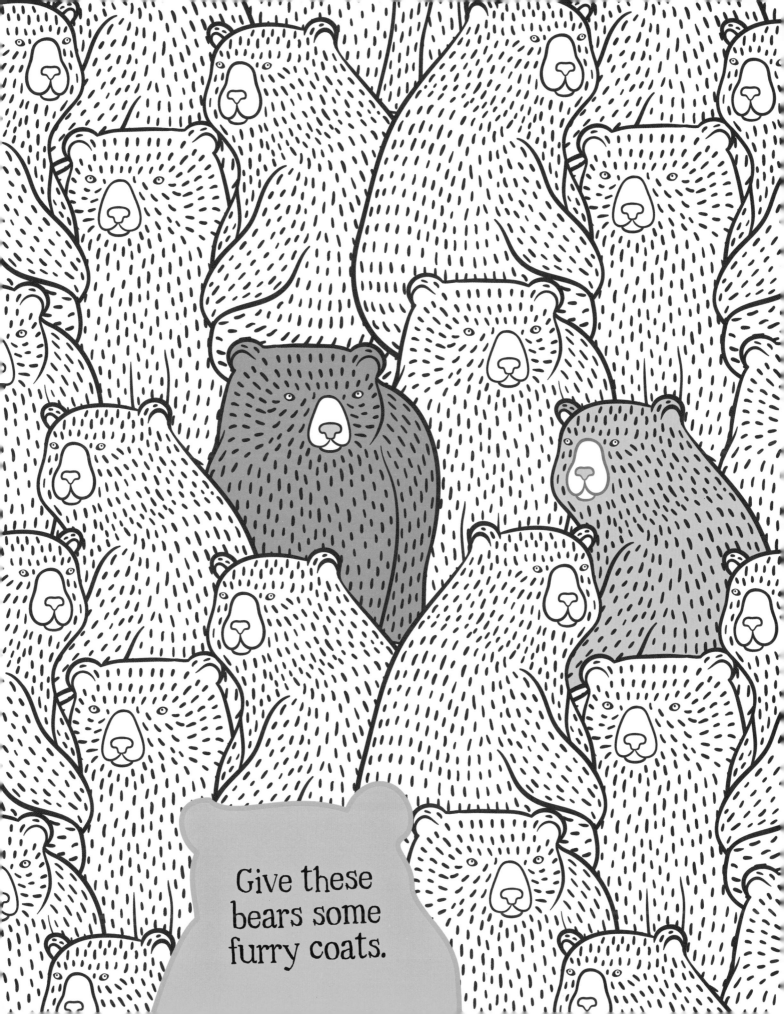

Give these
bears some
furry coats.

Color in this pair of Stegosaurus and draw some more.

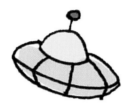

Draw what you think a UFO would look like!

Can you spot the gerbils?

Color the cool pattern.

Add some more towers to these castles, then color them in.

Fill this page with rockets and the planets they're flying past!

What do you think would make the perfect fairy pet? Draw it!

What would
you build?

Color in these water lilies.

Give these
pampered pugs
some pooch
accessories.

Complete this groovy pattern.

Draw an amazing
rabbit warren
for this bunny!

Color in the magical butterflies!

Doodle a pet dragon of your own!
Is it a fearsome fire-breather,
or an old softie?

ADOPT
A
DRAGON

Pick some snappy shades for these retro cameras!

Design a flag
for your
pirate ship!

Draw a friend
for this
rusty robot.

Draw the most amazing chicken coop you can imagine!

These frogs need some tropical colors!

Find the helicopters first, then color the rest...

...of these planes, trains, and automobiles!

Fill this page with lots of colorful medieval tents!

Color these insects, then cover the page with as many bugs as you can.

Stuff these jars with something nice, or something nasty!

Find the alien baby, then finish the scene!

EARTH

Draw more trees for
these dinos
to munch on.

Decorate these Chinese lanterns.

Fill the page with a fabulous firework display!

Draw an amazing park for the kids to play in.

Color in this pride of lions, then draw some other big cats.

What would your dream house look like?

Who is strong enough to pull this sword from the stone?

These leaves are multi-colored!

Draw the spookiest pumpkin
you can imagine...

These stones look spectacular!

Color these tasty treats!

Color in the pony and draw her a horsey friend.

Doodle a winter wonderland for these skiers...

Color in these woolly hats.

Who is this Ankylosaurus about to battle?

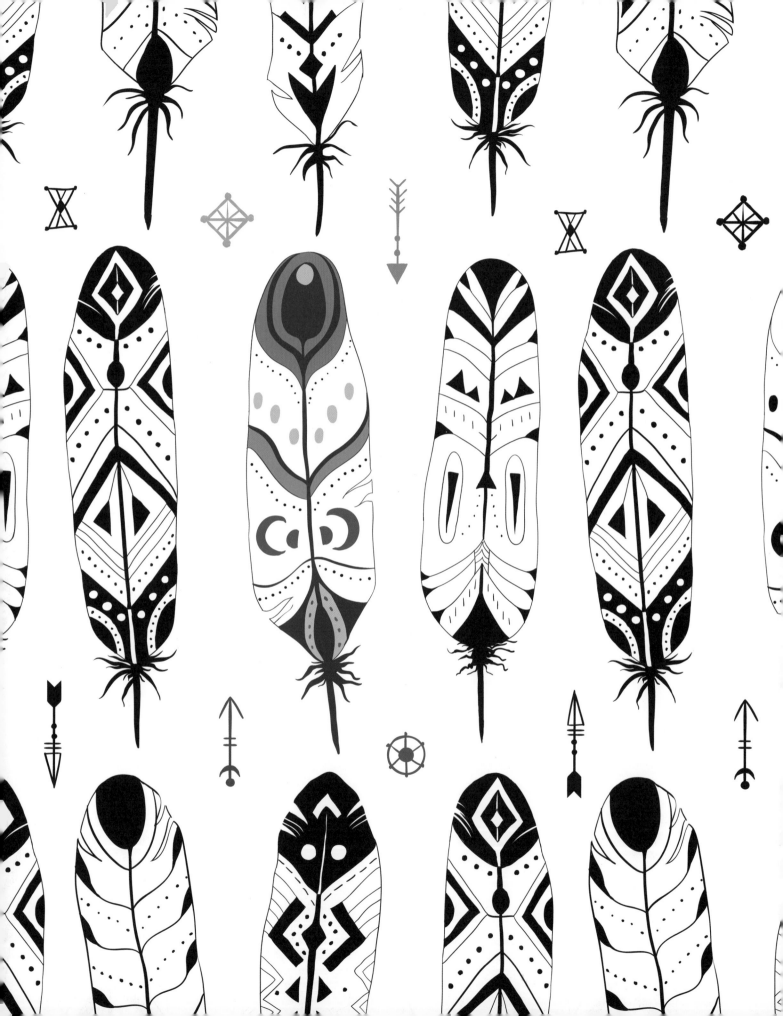

Doodle lots of
different tractors.

Draw the alien baby a carriage.

Anything goes, but it must be able to fly!

Draw a fabulous cake for this fairy's party!

Give these owls some beautiful feathers!

What is blocking this bulldozer's way?

What have these meerkats spotted on the horizon?

Design your
own pirate ship.

These astronauts are exploring an undiscovered planet. Draw what it looks like!

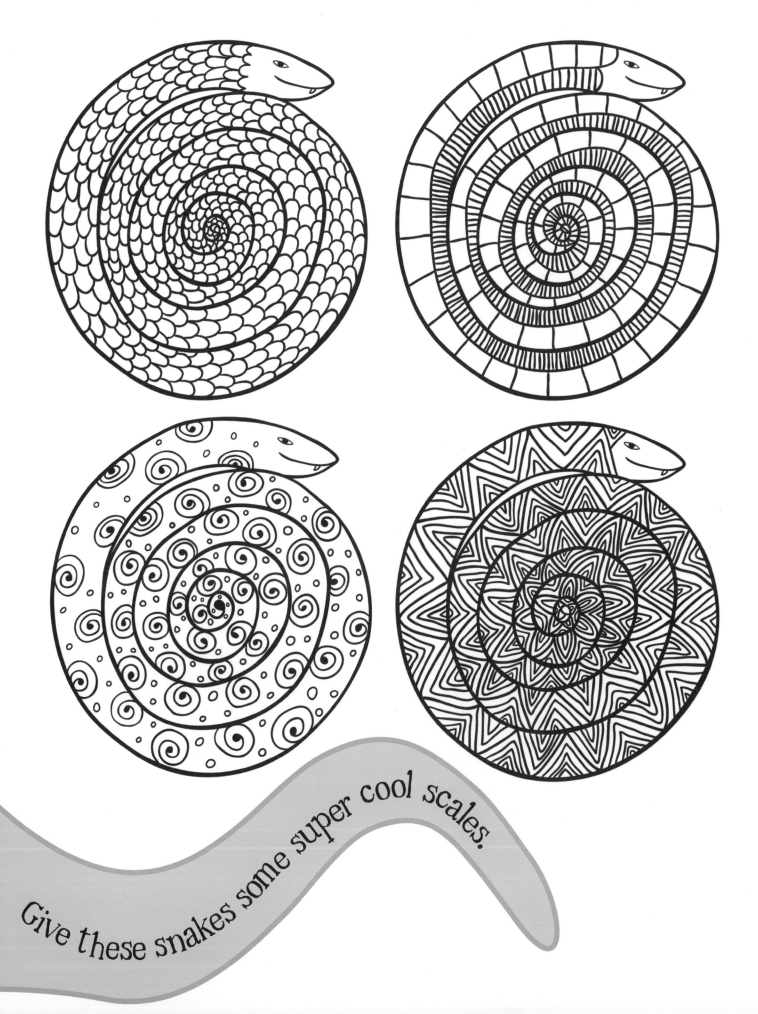

Give these snakes some super cool scales.

Cover this page with some beautiful bows, or some snazzy bow ties.

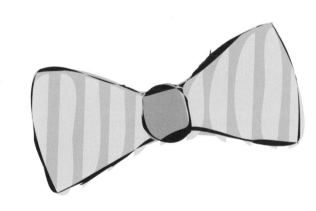

Find the
dragon in the tent...

...then color
in this scene!

Draw some cozy beds
and cute houses
for these pets.

Color in this super savannah scene!

Fill in this henna design, then add your own doodles to cover the page.

Draw the rest of the fairy band.

Color in this truck, and doodle a scrap yard full of useful bits and pieces.

Draw the sights these vehicles
are driving past.

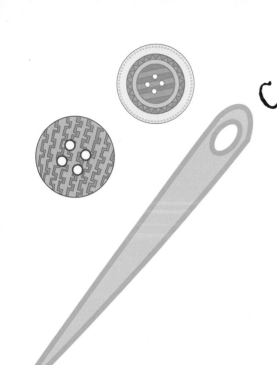

Cover this page with buttons of all shapes and sizes.

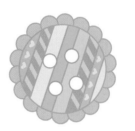

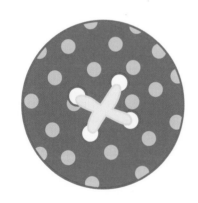

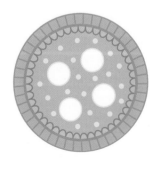

Color in these royal crowns, then draw one of your own!

Color the robots and give them some dancing partners!

Finish coloring in this bicycle pattern.

Fill this page with lots of satellites, spaceships, and planets.

Draw somewhere nice for these birds to perch.

Color in the locks...

...then color in the keys!

Color in this pirate scene!

Color the windows...

...and draw some people looking out.

Fill in this beautiful pattern.

Who are they cheering?

Color in the knights and draw some more.

What have these divers discovered?

Draw some more yummy donuts!

Color in the snowflakes.

Fill this page with more zebras, antelopes, and wildebeests.

What has this digger found underground?

Color in this magical scene!

Color in the clock faces!

Color in these cute woodland critters!

Fill in this floral pattern.

Color in these carousel horses.

Fill the page with tasty candies.

Complete this cool pattern.

Doodle some designs on these T-shirts.

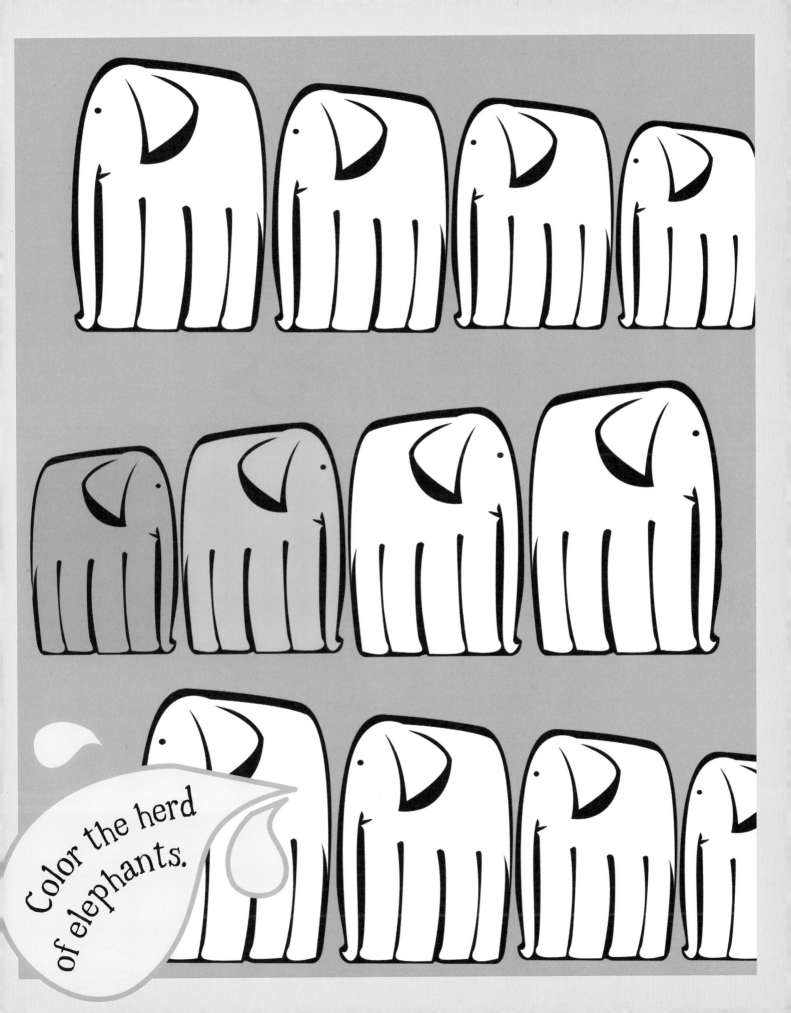

Color the herd of elephants.

Cover this page with a colony of penguins!

Turn this wintery scene into spring!

Draw a forest from a hedgehog's perspective!

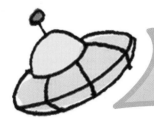

Who are they waving goodbye to?